The Sin and

Self-Love

Robert Cushman

Alpha Editions

This edition published in 2023

ISBN : 9789357935029

Design and Setting By
Alpha Editions
www.alphaedis.com
Email - info@alphaedis.com

BIOGRAPHICAL SKETCH,
BY
HON. JOHN DAVIS,
LATE JUDGE OF THE U. S. DISTRICT COURT,
MASSACHUSETTS DISTRICT.

ROBERT CUSHMAN, the author of the preceding discourse, was one of the most distinguished characters among that collection of worthies, who quitted England on account of their religious difficulties, and settled with Mr. *John Robinson*, their pastor in the city of Leyden, in Holland, in the year 1609. Proposing afterwards a removal to America in the year 1617, Mr. Cushman and Mr. John Carver, (afterwards the first Governor of New-Plymouth) were sent over to England, as their agents, to agree with the Virginia Company for a settlement, and to obtain, if possible, a grant of liberty of conscience in their intended plantation, from King James.

From this negotiation though conducted on their part with great discretion and ability, they returned unsuccessful to Leyden, in May 1618. They met with no difficulty indeed with the Virginia Company, who were willing to grant them sufficient territory, with as ample privileges as they could bestow: but the pragmatical James, the pretended vicegerent of the Deity, refused to grant them that liberty in religious matters, which was their principal object—when this persevering people finally determined to transport themselves to this country, relying upon James's promise that he would *connive* at, though not expressly *tolerate* them; Mr. Cushman was again dispatched to England in February 1619, with Mr. William Bradford, another of the company, to agree with the Virginia Company on the terms of their removal and settlement.

After much difficulty and delay, they obtained a patent in the September following, upon which part of the Church at Leyden, with their Elder Mr. Brewster determined to transport themselves as procure money, shipping and other necessaries for the voyage, and finally embarked with them at South-Hampton, August 5th, 1620. But the ship, in which he sailed, proving leaky, and after twice putting into port to repair, being finally condemned as unfit to perform the voyage, Mr. Cushman with his family, and a number of others were obliged, though reluctantly, to relinquish the voyage for that time and returned to London. Those in the other ship proceeded and made their final settlement at Plymouth in December 1620, where Mr. Cushman also arrived in the ship Fortune from London, on the 10th of November 1621, but took passage in the same ship back again, pursuant to the directions of the merchant adventurers in London, (who fitted out the ship and by whose assistance the first settlers were transported) to give them an account of the plantation. [A] He sailed from Plymouth December 13th, 1621, and arriving on the coast of England, the ship, with a cargo, valued at 500l. sterling, was taken by the French. Mr. Cushman, with the crew, was carried into France; but arrived in London in the February following. During his short residence at Plymouth, though a mere lay character, he delivered the preceding discourse, which was printed in London in 1622, and afterwards re-printed in Boston in 1724. And though his name is not prefixed to either edition, yet unquestionable tradition renders it certain that he was the author, and even transmits to us a knowledge of the spot where it was delivered. Mr. Cushman, though he constantly corresponded with his friends here, and was very serviceable to their interest in London—never returned to the country again, but while preparing for it was removed to a better, in the year 1626. The news of his death and Mr. Robinson's arrived at the same time at Plymouth, by Captain Standish, and seem to have been equally lamented by their bereaved and suffering friends there. He was zealously engaged in the prosperity of the plantation, a man of activity and enterprise, well versed in business, respectable in point of intellectual abilities, well accomplished in scriptural knowledge, an unaffected professor, and a steady sincere practiser of religion. The design of the following discourse was to keep up the noble flow of public spirit, which perhaps began then to abate, but which was necessary for their preservation and security.

After the death of Mr. Cushman, his family came over to New England. His son, Thomas Cushman, succeeded Mr. Brewster, as ruling elder of the Church of Plymouth, being ordained to that office in 1649. He was a man of good gifts, and frequently assisted in carrying on the public worship, preaching, and catechising. For it was one professed principle of that Church, in its first formation, 'to choose none for governing Elders, but such as were able to teach.' He continued in this office till he died, in 1691, in the eighty-fourth year of his age.

It seems to be a mistaken idea that Mr. Cushman started in the smaller vessel, which put back on account of its proving leaky. This mistake has arisen from the fact that Mr. C. was left in England in 1620, and did not come over in the Mayflower with the first emigrants. The fact is that Mr. Cushman procured 'the larger vessel,' the Mayflower, and its pilot at London and left in that vessel; but in consequence of the unsoundness of the smaller vessel, the Speedwell, it became necessary that part of the pilgrims should be left behind, and consequently Mr. Cushman, whom Gov. Bradford called 'the right hand with the adventurers,' and who 'for divers years had managed all our business with them to our great advantage,' was selected as one who would be best able to keep together that portion of the flock left behind. Although Mr. Cushman did not come over in the Mayflower, yet such was the respect for him among those who did come, that his name is placed at the head of those who came in that ship, in the allotment of land at a time when he was not in New England. [A]

N. B. S.

LETTER FROM JUDGE DAVIS.

BOSTON, DEC. 21, 1846.

Dear Sir:

Having communicated to me your intention of publishing a new edition of Robert Cushman's memorable discourse, delivered in Plymouth, 1621, together with the memoir of the author, which I prepared for the edition printed by Nathaniel Coverly in Plymouth, in 1785; I take the liberty to advise you to follow for your purpose that copy of the memoir which was inserted by the Rev. Dr. Belknap in the second volume of his American Biography, with the addition of some particulars respecting the family, especially of elder Thomas Cushman, son of Robert Cushman, and who, like his father, was held in high esteem by all his cotemporaries.

The original memoir prepared for the Plymouth edition, was anonymous. My highly esteemed friend the Rev. Dr. Belknap, in giving it a place in his valuable work was pleased to announce the name of the writer.

The remarks on the discourse originally accompanying the memoir, were prompted by views supposed to have been adopted by the Plymouth pioneers respecting property and civil polity, in which I was afterwards convinced I had made a mistake. I had adopted an opinion corresponding with that of Dr. Robertson and other writers, that misguided by their religious theories and in imitation of the primitive christians, they voluntarily threw all their property into a common stock. And that their difficulties and embarrassments were greatly enhanced by adopting, and perseveringly adhering to an impracticable system. But further inquiry induced the conviction that this conjecture was erroneous, and that the severe pressure they experienced, was in a great degree produced by the operation of their articles of agreement with the adventurers in England, which established a community of interest for seven years, and prevented the holding in severalty the fruits of their industry and enterprise.

These views of the subject, and an acknowledgement of my previous mistake, were expressed in a discourse delivered at Plymouth, in the year 1800, on the anniversary of the landing of the fathers. The Rev. Mr. Abbot of Beverly, afterwards, on a like occasion, without any knowledge of the contents of that discourse, which was not published, was led in his investigation of the subject, into a similar conclusion, and fully vindicated the pilgrims from the censures which had been expressed relative to this branch of their proceedings. The onerous connection with the merchant adventurers remained until 1627, when an amicable and satisfactory settlement was made with them by a purchase of all their interest in the concern. The sum contracted to be given for this purchase, was 1800 pounds sterling, payable by instalments of 200 pounds annually.

Thus says Governor Bradford in one of his letters:

"All now is become our own, as we say in the proverb, when our debts are paid. And doubtless this was a great mercy of God unto us, and a great means of peace and better subsistence, and wholly dashed all the plots and devices of our enemies, both there and here, who daily expected our ruin, dispersion and utter subversion by the same; but their hopes were thus far prevented though with great care and labor, we were left to struggle with the payment of the money."

Under these impressions I think it will be well for you to omit the insertion of the remarks above mentioned on Mr. Cushman's discourse. That discourse is a precious relic of ancient times, the sound sense, good advice, and pious spirit, which it manifests, will, it may be hoped, now, and in all future time, meet with approval and beneficial acceptance in our community.

The information contained in the note of your correspondent respecting Mr. Cushman's embarcation, and the assignment of land made to him in the colony, is believed to be correct.

Respectfully Your Ob't. Servant,
J. DAVIS.

To CHARLES EWER, Esq.

To his loving Friends the Adventurers for New-England.
TOGETHER
With all Well-Willers, and Well-wishers thereunto, Grace and Peace, &c.

NEW-ENGLAND, so called, not only (to avoid novelties) because Captain *Smith* hath so entitled it in his Description, but because of the resemblance that is in it, of *England* the native soil of Englishmen; it being much what the same for heat and cold in Summer and Winter, it being champaign ground, but no high mountains, somewhat like the soil in *Kent* and *Essex*; full of dales, and meadow ground, full of rivers and sweet springs, as *England* is. But principally, so far as we can yet find, it is an island, and near about the quantity of *England*, being cut out from the main land in *America*, as *England* is from the main of *Europe*, by a great arm of the sea, which entereth in forty degrees, and runneth up North West and by West, and goeth out either into the South-Sea, or else into the Bay of *Canada*. The certainty whereof, and secrets of which, we have not yet so found as that as eye-witnesses we can make narration thereof, but if God give time and means, we shall, ere long, discover both the extent of that river, together with the secrets thereof; and so try what territories, habitations, or commodities, may be found, either in it, or about it.

It pertaineth not to my purpose to speak any thing either in praise, or dispraise of the country; so it is by God's Providence, that a few of us are there planted to our content, and have with great charge and difficulty attained quiet and competent dwellings there. And thus much I will say for the satisfaction of such as have any thought of going hither to inhabit? That for men which have a large heart, and look after great riches, ease, pleasures, dainties, and jollity in this world (except they will live by other men's sweat, or have great riches) I would not advise them to come there, for as yet the country will afford no such matters: But if there be any who are content to lay out their estates, spend their time, labors, and endeavors, for the benefit of them that shall come after, and in desire to further the gospel among those poor heathens, quietly contenting themselves with such hardship and difficulties, as by God's Providence shall fall upon them, being yet young, and in their strength, such men I would advise and encourage to go, for their ends cannot fail them.

And if it should please God to punish his people in the Christian countries of *Europe*, (for their coldness, carnality, wanton abuse of the Gospel, contention, &c.) either by Turkish slavery, or by popish tyranny which God forbid, yet if the time be come, or shall come (as who knoweth) when Satan shall be let loose to cast out his floods against them, (*Rev. 12. 14. 15.*) here is a way opened for such as have wings to fly into this wilderness; and as by the dispersion of the Jewish church through persecution, the Lord brought in the fulness of the Gentiles, (*Act. 11. 20, 21.*) so who knoweth, whether now by tyranny and affliction, he suffereth to come upon them, he will not by little and little chase them even amongst the heathens, that so a light may rise up in the dark, (*Luke 2. 32.*) and the kingdom of Heaven be taken from them which now have it, and given to a people that shall bring forth the fruit of it. (*Mat. 21. 43.*) This I leave to the judgment of the godly wise, being neither prophet nor son of a prophet, (*Amos 7. 14.*) but considering God's dealing of old, (*2 Kings 17, 23.*) and seeing the name of Christian to be very great, but the true nature thereof almost quite lost in all degrees and sects, I cannot think but that there is some judgment not far off, and that God will shortly, even of stones, raise up children unto *Abraham*. (*Mat. 3. 5.*)

And who so rightly considereth what manner of entrance, abiding, and proceedings, we have had among these poor heathens since we came hither, will easily think, that God has some great work to do towards them.

They were wont to be the most cruel and treacherous people in all these parts, even like lions, but to us they have been like lambs, so kind, so submissive, and trusty, as a man may truly say, many christians are not so kind, nor sincere.

They were very much wasted of late, by reason of a great mortality that fell amongst them three years since, which together with their own civil dissentions and bloody wars, hath so wasted them, as I think the twentieth person is scarce left alive, and those that are left, have their courage much abated, and their countenance is dejected, and they seem as a people affrighted. And though when we came first into the Country, we were few, and many of us were sick, and many died by reason of the cold and wet, it being the depth of winter, and we having no houses, nor shelter, yet when there was not six able persons among us, and that they came daily to us by hundreds, with their *sachems* or *kings*, and might in one hour have made a dispatch of us, yet such a fear was upon them, as that they never offered us the least injury in word or deed. And by reason of one *Tisquanto*, that lives amongst us, that can speak English, we have daily commerce with their kings, and can know what is done or intended towards us among the savages; also we can acquaint them with our courses and purposes, both human and religious. And the greatest commander of the country, called *Massasoit*, cometh often to visit us, tho' he lives 50 miles from us, often sends us presents, he having with many other of their governors, promised, yea, subscribed obedience to our sovereign Lord King James, and for his cause to spend both strength and life. And we for our parts, through God's grace, have with that equity, justice, and compassion, carried ourselves towards them, as that they have received much favor, help, and aid from us, but never the least injury or wrong by us. [A] We found the place where we live empty, the people being all dead and gone away, and none living near by 8 or 10 miles; and though in the time of some hardship we found (travelling abroad) near 8 bushels of corn hid up in a cave, and knew no owners of it, yet afterwards hearing of the owners of it, we gave them (in their estimation) double the value of it. Our care hath been to maintain peace amongst them, and have always set ourselves against such of them as used any rebellion, or treachery against their governors, and not only threatened such, but in some sort paid them their due deserts; and when any of them are in want, as often they are in the winter, when their corn is done, we supply them to our power, and have them in our houses eating and drinking, and warming themselves, which thing (though it be something a trouble to us) yet because they should see and take knowledge of our labors, order and diligence, both for this life and a better, we are content to bear it, and we find in many of them, especially, of the younger sort, such a tractable disposition, both to religion and humanity, as that if we had means to apparel them, and wholly to retain them with us (as their desire is) they would doubtless in time prove serviceable to God and man, and if ever God send us means we will bring up hundreds of their children, both to labor and learning.

But leaving to speak of them till a further occasion be offered; if any shall marvel at the publishing of this treatise in *England*, seeing there is no want of good books, but rather want of men to use good books, let them know, that the especial end is, that we may keep those motives in memory for ourselves, and those that shall come after, to be a remedy against self love the bane of all societies. And that we also might testify to our Christian countrymen, who judge diversly of us, that though we be in a heathen country, yet the grace of Christ is not quenched in us, but we still hold and teach the same points of faith, mortification, and sanctification, which we have heard and learned, in a most ample and large manner in our own country. If any shall think it too rude and unlearned for this curious age, let them know, that to paint out the Gospel in plain and flat English, amongst a company of plain Englishmen (as we are) is the best and most profitablest teaching; and we will study plainness, not curiosity, neither in things human, nor heavenly. If any error or unsoundness be in it, (as who knoweth) impute it to that frail man which endited it, which professeth to know nothing as he ought to know it. I have not set down my name, partly because I seek no name, and principally, because I would have nothing esteemed by names, for I see a number of evils to arise through names, when the persons are either famous, or infamous, and God and man is often injured; if any good or profit arise to thee in the receiving of it, give

God the praise and esteem me as a son of *Adam*, subject to all such frailties as other men are.

And you my loving friends the adventurers to this plantation; as your care has been, first to settle religion here, before either profit or popularity, so I pray you, go on, to do it much more, and be careful to send godly men, though they want some of that worldly policy which this world hath in her own generation, and so though you lose, the Lord shall gain. I rejoice greatly in your free and ready minds to your powers, yea, and beyond your powers to further this work, that you thus honor God with your riches, and I trust you shall be repayed again double and treble in this world, yea, and the memory of this action shall never die, but above all adding unto this (as I trust you do) like freeness in all other God's services both at home and abroad, you shall find reward with God, ten thousand-fold surpassing all that you can do or think; be not therefore discouraged, for no labor is lost, nor money spent which is bestowed for God, your ends were good, your success is good, and your profit is coming, even in this life, and in the life to come much more: and what shall I say now, a word to men of understanding sufficeth, pardon I pray you my boldness, read over the ensuing treatise, and judge wisely of the poor weakling, and the Lord, the God of land and sea, stretch out his arm of protection over you and us, and over all our lawful and good enterprizes, either this, or any other way.

Plymouth in New-England, December 12, 1621.

They offer us to dwell where we will. [A]

A SERMON
Preached at PLYMOUTH, in New England, 1621.

1 CORINTHIANS, 10. 24.
LET NO MAN SEEK HIS OWN: BUT EVERY MAN
ANOTHER'S WEALTH.

The occasion of these words of the Apostle *Paul*, was because of the abuses which were in the Church of *Corinth*. Which abuses arose chiefly through swelling pride, self-love and conceitedness, for although this church was planted by *Paul* and watered by *Apollos*, and much increased by the Lord; yet the sower of tares was not wanting to stir up evil workers and fleshly minded hypocrites, under a shew of godliness, and with angel-like holiness in appearance, to creep in amongst them to disturb their peace, try their soundness, and prove their constancy. And this the Apostle complains of very often: as first, in their carnal divisions, chap. 1. then in their extolling their eloquent teachers, and despising *Paul*, chap. 4. Then in their offensive going to Law, before the heathen judges, chap. 6. Then in eating things offered to idols, to the destroying of the tender consciences of their brethren, chap. 8. Then in their insatiable love feasts, in the time and place of their church meetings, the rich which could together feed to fulness, despising and contemning the poor, that had not to lay it on as they had, chap. 11. Finally in both the epistles, he very often nippeth them for their pride, and self-love, straitness and censoriousness, so that in the last chapter he willeth them again and again to prove, try and examine themselves, to see whether Christ were in them or not, for howsoever many of them seemed, as thousands do at this day to soar aloft, and go with full sail to Heaven: yet as men that row in boats, set their faces one way, when yet their whole body goeth apace another way: so there are many which set such a face upon religion, and have their mouth full of great swelling words: as if they would even blow open the doors of heaven, despising all humble minded and broken-hearted people, as weak, simple, sottish, &c. when yet notwithstanding, these blusterers, which seem to go so fast, and leave all others behind them, if like these glosing *Corinthians*, they carry affectedly their own glory with them, and seem thus to stand for the glory of God. What do they else but join flesh to spirit, serving not God for nought, but for wages, and so serving their bellies, whose end will be damnation, except a speedy and sound remedy be thought of, which remedy is even that which our Saviour teacheth the rich young gallant, and which *Paul* here prescribeth, in willing them not to seek their own, but every man another's wealth, which physic is as terrible to carnal professors, as abstinence from drink is to a man that hath the dropsy; and it is a sure note, that a man is sick of this disease of self-love, if this be grievous to him, as appeareth in the man whom Christ bid sell that he had, and he went away very sorrowful, yet surely this vein must be pricked, and this humor let out, else it will spoil all, it will infect both soul and body, yea, and the contagion of it is such (as we shall see anon) as will even hazard the welfare of that society where self seekers and self lovers are.

As God then did direct this Apostle to lay down this brief direction as a remedy for that evil in *Corinth*, so you may think it is by God's special providence, that I am now to speak unto you from this text: and say in your hearts, surely something is amiss this way: let us know it and amend it.

The parts of this text are two. 1. A *Dehortation*. 2. An *Exhortation*. The Dehortation, *Let no man seek his own*. The Exhortation, *But every man another's wealth*.

In handling of which, I will first, open the words. Secondly, gather the doctrine. Thirdly illustrate the doctrine by scriptures, experience and reasons. Fourthly apply the same, to every one his portion.

The proper drift of the Apostle here is not to tax the *Corinthians*, for seeking their own evil ends in evil actions, but for aiming at themselves, and their own benefits in actions lawful, and that appeareth in the former verse, where he saith, *All things are lawful, &c.* viz. all such things as now we speak of, to eat any of God's creatures, offered to idols or not, to feast and be merry together, to shew love and kindness to this or that person, &c. but when by such means we seek ourselves, and have not a charitable loving and reverent regard of others, then they are unexpedient, unprofitable, yea unlawful, and must be forborne, and he that hath not learned to deny himself even the very use of lawful things, when it tendeth to the contempt, reproach, grief, offence and shame of his other brethren and associates, hath learned nothing aright, but is, apparently, a man that seeks himself, and against whom the Apostle here dealeth most properly.

The manner of the speech, may seem as counsel left at liberty: as Mat. 27. 49. And in our ordinary speech, we think they be but weak charges, which are thus delivered, let a man do this, or let him do that. But we must learn the apostle's modesty, and know that whatsoever the terms seem to imply, yet even this and other the like in this epistle, are most absolute charges: as, *Let a man esteem of us, as the ministers of Christ, chap. 41*. That is, a man ought so to esteem of us. *Let a man examine himself, 1 Cor. 11. 28*. That is, as if he said, a man must examine himself. *Let your women keep silence in the churches, 1 Cor. 14, 34*. that is, they ought so to do.

The meaning then summarily is, as if he said, the bane of all these mischiefs which arise among you is, that men are too cleaving to themselves and their own matters, and disregard and contemn all others: and therefore I charge you, let this self seeking be left off, and turn the stream another way, namely, seek the good of your brethren, please them, honor them, reverence them, for otherwise it will never go well amongst you.

Obj. But doth not the Apostle elsewhere say? *That he, which careth not for his own, is worse than an infidel. 1 Tim. 5. 8.*

Ans. True, but by (own) there, he meaneth properly, a man's kindred, and here by (own) he meaneth properly a man's self.

Secondly, he there especially taxeth such as were negligent in their labors and callings, and so made themselves unable to give relief and entertainment to such poor widows and orphans as were of their own flesh and blood.

Thirdly, be it so, that some man should even neglect his own self, his own wife, children, friends, &c. And give that he had to strangers, that were but some rare vice, in some one unnatural man, and if this vice slay a thousand, self-love slayeth ten thousands.

And this the wisdom of God did well foresee, and hath set no caveats in the scriptures either to tax men, or forewarn them from loving others, neither saith God any where, let no man seek out the good of another, but let no man seek his own, and every where in the scriptures he hath set watch words against self good, self-profit, self-seeking, &c. And thus the sense being cleared, I come to the doctrine.

Doct. 1. *All men are too apt and ready to seek themselves too much, and to prefer their own matters and causes beyond the due and lawful measure, even to excess and offence against God, yea danger of their own souls.*

And this is true not only in wicked men which are given over of God to vile lusts, as *Absalom* in getting favor in his father's court: *Jereboam*, in settling his kingdom fast in *Samaria*, *Ahab* in vehement seeking *Naboth's* vineyard, but men, otherwise godly, have through frailty been foiled herein, and many thousands which have a shew of godliness, are lovers of themselves: *David* was about to seek himself when he was going to kill *Naball: Asa* in putting *Hanani* in prison: *Josiah* when he would go to war with *Necho*, against the counsel of God, and reason; *Peter* when he dissembled about the ceremonies of the law, yea and *Paul* complains of all his followers (*Timothy* excepted) that they sought their own too inordinately.

And why else are these caveats in the scriptures, but to warn the godly that they be not tainted herewith? as, *Look not every man on his own things, but on the things of another: Love seeketh not her own things. Be not desirous of vain glory, &c.* Philip. 2. 4. 1 Cor. 13. 6. Gal. 5. 26.

Yea and doth not experience teach, that even amongst professors of religion, almost all the love and favor that is shewed unto others is with a secret aim at themselves, they will take pains to do a man good, provided that he will take twice so much for them, they will give a penny so as it may advantage them a pound, labor hard so as all the profit may come to themselves, else they are heartless and feeble. The vain and corrupt heart of man cannot better be resembled then by a belly-god, host, or innkeeper which welcometh his guests with smilings, and salutations, and a thousand welcomes, and rejoiceth greatly to have their company to dice, cards, eat, drink, and be merry, but should not the box be paid, the pot be filling, and the money telling, all this while, the epicure's joy would soon be turned into sorrow, and his smiles turned into frowns, and the door set open, and their absence craved: even so men blow the bellows hard, when they have an iron of their own a heating, work hard whilst their own house is in building, dig hard whilst their own garden is in planting, but is it so as the profit must go wholly or partly to others; their hands wax feeble, their hearts wax faint, they grow churlish, and give cross answers, like *Naball*, they are sour, discontent, and nothing will please them. And where is that man to be found, that will disperse abroad, and cast his bread upon the waters, that will lend, looking for nothing again, that will do all duties to other freely and cheerfully in conscience to God, and love unto men, without his close and secret ends or aiming at himself; such a man, out of doubt, is a black swan, a white crow almost, and yet such shall stand before God with boldness at the last day, when others which have sought themselves, though for love of themselves they have sought heaven, yea, and through self-love persuaded themselves they should find it, yet wanting love unto others, they will be found as sounding brass, and as a tinkling cimbal, and whilst they have neglected others, and not cared how others live, so as themselves may fare well, they will be found amongst them, that the Lord will say unto, *I know you not, depart ye cursed into everlasting fire,* Mat. 25. 41. 42.

But that I may not walk in generalities, the particular ways by which men seek their own are these: First, such as are covetous, seek their own by seeking riches, wealth, money, as *Felix* pretending love unto *Paul,* sent for him often, but it was in hope of money. Many there are who say, *who will shew us any good,* Psal. 4. 7. And pretend religion, as some of the Jews did the keeping of the Sabbath, which yet cried out, when will the Sabbath be done, that we may sell corn, and get gain; if a man can tell how to get gold out of a flint, and silver out of the adamant, no pains shall be spared, no time shall be neglected, for gold is their hope, and the wedge of gold is their confidence, their hearts are set upon the pelf of this world, and for love of it, all things are let slip, even all duties to God or men, they care not how basely they serve, how wretchedly they neglect all others, so as they may get wealth: pinch who will, and wring who will; all times are alike with them, and they run for the bribe and *Gehazie*; and this is the first way that men seek their own.

Now the contrary is seen in *Nehemiah*, who when the people were hard put to it, and the land raw, he took not the duties which were due to him being a magistrate, he bought no land, nor grew rich, for it was no time: but he maintained at his table many of his brethren the Jews, and so spent even his own proper goods. And *Paul* sought no man's gold nor silver, but though he had authority, yet he took not bread of the churches, but labored with his hands: and why? It was no time to take, some churches were poor and stood in want, as *Thessalonica*, others were in danger to be preyed upon by covetous belly-gods, as *Corinth*: and therefore he saw it no fit time now to take any thing of them.

And indeed here is the difference between a covetous worldling, and an honest thrifty Christian, it is lawful sometimes for men to gather wealth, and grow rich, even as there was a time for *Joseph* to store up corn, but a godly and sincere Christian will see when this time is, and will not hoard up when he seeth others of his brethren and associates to want, but then is a time, if he have any thing to fetch it out and disperse it, but the covetous gathers goods, he like *Achan* covets all that he seeth; and neglects no time, but gathers still and holds all fast, and if it were to save the life of his brother, his bags must not be diminished, nor his chests lighted, nor his field set to sale, gather as much as he can, but it's death to diminish the least part of it.

2. The second way by which men seek their own, is when they seek ease, or pleasure, as the *Scribes* and *Pharisees*, who would not touch the burden with one of their fingers; for there is a generation, which think to have more in this world then *Adam's* felicity in innocency, being born (as they think) to take their pleasures, and their ease, let the roof of the house drop through, they stir not; let the field be overgrown with weeds, they care not, they must not foul their hand, nor wet their foot, it's enough for them to say, Go you, not let us go, though never so much need; such idle drones, are intollerable in a settled commonwealth, much more in a commonwealth which is but as it were in the bud; of what earth I pray thee art thou made, of any better than the other of the sons of *Adam*? And canst thou see other of thy brethren toil their hearts out, and thou sit idle at home, or takest thy pleasure abroad? Remember the example of *Uriah*, who would not take his ease nor his pleasure, though the King required him, and why? Because his brethren, his associates, better men than himself (as he esteemed them) were under hard labors and conditions, lay in the field in tents, caves, &c.

3. The third way is when men seek their own bellies, as some did in the Apostles' times, which went about with new doctrines and devices, knowing that the people had itching ears, and would easily entertain and willingly feed such novelists, which brought in dissensions, schisms, and contentions, and such were rocks, or pillars in their love-feasts, as *Jude* speaketh, *ver. 12.* They were shadows in God's service, but when feasting came, then they were substances, then they were in their element. And certainly there are some men which shape even their religion, human state, and all, even as the belly cheer is best, and that they must have, else all heart and life is gone; let all conscience, care of others go, let *Lazarus* starve at the gate, let *Joseph's* affliction be increased, they must have their dishes, their dainties, or no content. The contrary was seen in *Nehemiah*, who would not take his large portion allotted to the governor, because he knew it went short with others of his brethren; and *Uriah* would not receive the King's present, and go banquet with his wife, because he knew the whole host his brethren were fain to snap short in the fields.

And the difference between a temperate good man, and a belly-god is this: A good man will not eat his morsels alone, especially, if he have better than others, but if by God's providence, he have gotten some meat which is better than ordinary, and better than his other brethren, he can have no rest in himself, except he make others partake with him. But a belly-god will slop all in his own throat, yea, though his neighbor come in and behold him eat, yet his griple-gut shameth not to swallow all. And this may be done sometimes, as well in mean fare as in greater dainties, for all countries afford not alike.

4. The fourth way by which men seek their own, is by seeking outward honor, fame and respect with men; as King *Saul* when he had lost all respect and favor with God, then thought to give content to his heart by being honored before the Elders of the people; and it is wonderful to see how some men are *desirous of vain glory, Gal.* 5. 26. And how earnestly they seek praise, favor, and respect with men, and can have no quiet longer than their worldly favor lasteth, and that they will have what dishonor soever come to God, or disgrace unto men, yea, they will disgrace, reproach, and disdain others, to gain honor and advancement to themselves, yea, they will make bold with the Scriptures and Word of God, to wrest and wring, and slight it over for their credit's sake. And let a man mark some men's talk, stories, discourses, &c. and he shall see their whole drift is to extol and set out themselves, and get praise and commendation of men.

Now the contrary was seen in *Paul*, he saith, *He needed no letters of commendations*, 2 Cor. 3. 2. And again, *He is not affected with men's praise*, 1 Cor. 10. 12. And here is indeed the difference between an humble-minded Christian, and a proud self-lover; an humble man often hath praise, as

David, Hezekiah, and *Josiah,* but he seeks it not, he desires it not, he is content to go without it, he loves not the praise of men, for he knows it but froth and vanity: but a proud self-lover, he seeks it still, get it or not get it, and if he get it he is fully satisfied, if he get it not he hangs his head like a bull-rush, and hath no comfort.

5. The fifth way by which men seek their own, is *by seeking to have their wills;* as the wrong doers in *Corinth,* who thought it not enough to do wrong and harm to their brethren, but to have their wills enough of them, drew them before the Heathen magistrates.

And truly some men are so prince-like, or rather Papal, that their very will and word is become a law, and if they have said it, it must be so, else there is no rest or quietness to be had, let never so many reasons be brought to the contrary, it is but fighting with the wind. They are like the obstinate Jews, who when against God's law, and reason, they asked a King, though *Samuel* shewed them that it would turn in the end to their own smart, yet still held the conclusion, and said, nay, *But we will have a King,* 1 Sam. 8. 19. Thus men are caught by their own words, and insnared by the straitness of their own hearts, and it is death to them not to have their wills, and howsoever sometimes (like *Jezebel*) they are cut short of their purposes, yet self-willed men will strut and swell like *Absalom,* saying neither *good nor bad,* 2 Sam. 13. 22. but hope for the day, and threaten like prophane *Esau,* Gen. 27. 41. Now the contrary is seen in *David,* though a prince, a captain, a warrior, who having said, yea sworn, that he would kill *Nabal,* and all his family that day, yet upon reasonable counsel given, and that by a weak woman, he changed his mind, altered his purpose, and returned, without striking one stroke, an example rare, and worthy imitation; and when men are sick of will, let them think of *David,* it was his grace and honor to go back from his word and practice, when reason came. So was it *Herod's* disgrace and shame to hold his word and will against reason and conscience, *Math. 14. 8, 9.*

Quest. But some men happily will say unto me, It is true, that men seek their own by all these ways, *But what should be the reason and cause of this? that men seek so earnestly themselves, in seeking riches, honor, ease, belly-cheer, will, &c. something there is that carrieth them.*

Ans. True, and the reasons and causes are specially these three:

First, pride and high conceitedness, when men overvalue themselves: and this made *Absalom* to seek his father's kingdom, because he thought himself worthy of it. *2 Sam. 15. 4.* This made *Haman* so sore vexed, because *Mordecai* bowed not to him, because he highly valued himself, *Esther, 3. 5.*

And surely that which a man valueth much, he giveth much respect to, and so it is a sure sign that a man loves himself most when he giveth most to himself; and some intolerable proud persons even think all the world is for them, and all their purposes and endeavors shew what a large conceit they have of themselves.

Secondly, want of due consideration and valuation of other men's endowments, abilities and deserts; when men pass those things by, though they have both seen, heard, and felt them; as *Pharaoh's* butler forgot *Joseph's* eminency when he was restored to his place, *Gen. 40. 23.* So men used to write their own good actions in brass, but other men's in ashes, never remembering nor considering the pains, labor, good properties, &c. which others have, and so they have no love to them, but only to themselves; as if God had made all other men unreasonable beasts, and them only reasonable men.

Thirdly, want of heavenly conversation, and spiritual eye to behold the glory, greatness, and majesty, and goodness of God; as the Queen of *Sheba*, thought highly of her own glory, wisdom and happiness, till she saw *Solomon's* wisdom and glory, and then she cried out, not of the happiness of her own servants, but of his servants that stood before him, *1 Kings 10. 7, 8.* And verily, if men were conversant courtiers in Heaven, they would cry out with *Paul*, Rom. 11. 33. *Oh the depth of the riches, wisdom, and knowledge of God, &c.* and would be ashamed of their own sinfulness, nakedness and misery; for, as countrymen which never saw the state of cities, nor the glory of courts, admire even their own country Orders: And as the savages here which are clad in skins, and creep in woods and holes, think their own brutish and inhuman life the best, which if they saw and did rightly apprehend the benefit of comely humanity, the sweetness of religion and the service of God, they would even shamefully hide themselves from the eye of all noble Christians. Even so, if men in serious contemplation, by the eye of faith, would behold the glory of God, and what great riches, beauty, fulness, perfection, power, dignity and greatness is in God, they would leave admiring of themselves, and seeking of themselves, and would say with *David, What am I? And what is my father's house? that thou shouldest thus bless me?* 2 Sam. 7. 18. Yea *What is man? or the son of man that thou so regardest him?* Psal. 8. 3.

But it is time to come to apply these things more particularly to ourselves, and see what Use is to be made of them:

Use 1. Is it so, that God seeth a proneness in all the sons of *Adam*, to seek themselves too much, and hath given them warnings and watch-words thereof, as we have heard, and doth experience confirm it? Then hence are reproved a number of men, who think they can never shew love enough to themselves, nor seek their own enough, but think all cost, charges, cherishing, praise, honor, &c. too little for them, and no man needeth to say to them, as *Peter* did to Christ, *favor thy self*; but if they do a little for another man, they account it a great matter, though it be but a morsel of bread, or a single penny; but no varieties of dainties is too good for them, no silk, purple, cloth, or stuff is too good to clothe them, the poor man's idleness and ill husbandry is oft thrown in his dish, but their own carnal delights and fleshy wantonness is never thought upon: and why? Because they think even God and man owes all to them, but they owe nothing to none. Why, thou foolish and besotted man, hath not the Holy Ghost read it in the very face of every son of *Adam*, that he is too apt to seek his own, and art thou wiser than God, to think thou never seekest thine own enough? or dreamest thou that thou art made of other, and better mettle than other men are? Surely, I know no way to escape, having of corruption to thy father, and the worm to thy sister and brother. And if God had any where in all the Scriptures said, love thyself, make much of thyself, provide for one, &c. there were some reason for thee to take up the niggard's proverbs, *Every man for himself, and God for us all; Charity beginneth at home, &c.* But God never taught thee these things; No, they are Satan's positions. Doth God ever commend a man for carnal love of himself? Nay he brands it, and disgraceth it, as *self love, taking thought for the flesh; loving of pleasure, &c.* Rom. 13. 14, 2 Tim. 34.

Obj. It is a point of good natural policy, for a man to care and provide for himself.

Ans. Then the most fools have most natural policy, for you see not the greatest drones and novices, either in church, or commonwealth, to be the greatest scratchers and scrapers, and gatherers of riches? Are they not also for the most part, best fed and clad? And live they not most easily? What shall I say? Even hogs, dogs, and brute beasts know their own ease, and can seek that which is good for themselves; and what doth this shifting, progging, and fat feeding which some use, more resemble any thing than the fashion of hogs? And so let it be what natural policy it will.

Use 2. If God see this disease of self-love so dangerous in us, then it standeth us all in hand to suspect ourselves, and so to seek out the root of this disease, that it may be cured. If a learned physician, shall see by our countenance and eye, that we have some dangerous disease growing on us, our hearts will smite us, and we will bethink ourselves where the most grief lieth, and how it should come, whether with cold, heat, surfeit, over-flowing of blood, or through grief, melancholy, or any such way, and every man will bestir himself to get rid of it, and will prevent always that which feeds the disease, and cherish all courses that would destroy it.

Now, how much more ought we to bestir ourselves, for this matter of self love, since God himself hath cast all our waters, and felt all our pulses, and pronounceth us all dangerously sick of this disease? Believe it, God cannot lie, nor be deceived; He that made the heart, doth not he know it? Let every man's heart smite him, and let him fall to the examination of himself and see first, whether he love not riches and worldly wealth too much, whether his heart be not too jocund at the coming of it in, and too heavy at the going of it out, for if you find it so there is great danger, if thou canst not buy as if thou possessed not, and use this world as though thou used it not, (*1 Cor. 7. 30, 31.*) thou art sick, and had need to look to it. So, if thou lovest thine ease and pleasure, see whether thou can be content to receive at God's hands evil as well as good, (*Job 2. 10.*) whether thou have learned as well to abound as to want, (*Phil. 4. 10.*) as well to endure hard labor, as to live at ease; and art as willing to go to the house of mourning as to the house of mirth, (*Eccl. 7. 6.*) for, else, out of doubt, thou lovest thy carnal pleasure and ease too much.

Again, see whether thy heart cannot be as merry, and thy mind as joyful, and thy countenance as cheerful, with coarse fare, with pulse, with bread and water (if God offer thee no better, nor the times afford other) as if thou had the greatest dainties: (*Dan. 1. 15.*) So also whether thou can be content as well with scorns of men, when thou hast done well, as with their praises, so if thou can with comfort and good conscience say, I pass little for man's judgment; whether thou can do thy duty that God requireth, and despise the shame, referring thyself unto God, for if thou be disheartened, discouraged, and weakened in any duty because of men's dispraises, its a sign thou lovest thyself too much.

So for the will, if thou can be content to give way even from that which thou hast said shall be, yea, vowed shall be, when better reason cometh, and hast that reverence of other men, as that when it standeth but upon a matter of will, thou art as willing their wills should stand as thine, and art not sad, churlish, or discontented, (*1 Kings 21. 4.*) but cheerful in thine heart, though thy will be crossed, it is a good sign, but if not, thou art sick of a self-will, and must purge it out. I the rather press these things, because I see many men both wise and religious, which yet are so tainted with this pestilent self-love, as that it is in them even as a dead fly to the apothecaries' ointment, spoiling the efficacy of all their graces, making their lives uncomfortable to themselves, and unprofitable to others, being neither fit for church nor commonwealth, but have even their very souls in hazard thereby, and therefore who can say too much against it.

It is reported, that there are many men gone to that other plantation in *Virginia*, which, whilst they lived in *England*, seemed very religious, zealous, and conscionable; and have now lost even the sap of grace, and edge to all goodness; and are become mere worldlings. This testimony I believe to be partly true, and amongst many causes of it, this self-love is not the least. It is indeed a matter of some commendation for a man to remove himself out of a thronged place into a wide wilderness; to take in hand so long and dangerous a journey, to be an instrument to carry the Gospel and humanity among the brutish heathen; but there may be many goodly shews and glosses and yet a pad in the straw, men may make a great appearance of respect unto God, and yet but dissemble with him, having their own lusts carrying them: and, out of doubt, men that have taken in hand hither to come, out of discontentment in regard of their estates in *England*; and aiming at great matters here, affecting it to be gentlemen, landed men, or hoping for office, place, dignity, or fleshly liberty; let the shew be what it will, the substance is naught, and that bird of self-love which was hatched at home, if it be not looked to, will eat out the life of all grace and goodness: and though men have escaped the danger of the sea, and that cruel mortality, which swept away so many of our loving friends and brethren; yet except they purge out this self-love, a worse mischief is prepared for them: And who knoweth whether God in mercy have delivered those just men which here departed, from the evils to come; and from unreasonable men, in whom there neither was, nor is, any comfort, but grief, sorrow, affliction, and misery, till they cast out this spawn of self-love.

But I have dwelt too long upon this first part; I come now to the second, which concerns an Exhortation, as I shewed you, in the Division.

But every man another's wealth.

In direct opposition, he should say, *Let every man seek another's*, but the first part being compared with the latter, and (*seek*) being taken out of the former and put to the latter, and (*wealth*) taken out or rather implied, in the former, the whole sentence is thus resolved, *Let no man seek his own wealth, but let every man seek another's wealth.*

And the word here translated *wealth*, is the same with that in *Rom. 13. 4*, and may not be taken only for riches, as Englishmen commonly understand it, but for all kinds of benefits, favors, comforts either for soul or body; and so here again, as before you must understand an Affirmative Commandment, as the Negative was before: and least any should say, If I may not seek my own good, I may do nothing; Yes saith *Paul*, I'll tell thee, thou shalt seek the good of another, whereas now all thy seeking helps but one, by this means thou shalt help many: and this is further enforced by these two circumstances, (no man) may seek his own, be he rich, learned, wise, &c. *But every man must seek the good of another.*

The point of instruction is taken from the very letter and phrase, viz.

Doct. 2. *A man* must *seek the good, the wealth, the profit of others.*

I say he *must* seek it, he must seek the comfort, profit and benefit of his neighbor, brother, associate, &c. His own good he need not seek, it will offer itself to him every hour; but the good of others must be sought, a man must not stay from doing good to others till he is sought unto, pulled and hauled, (as it were) like the unjust judge, for every benefit that is first craved, cometh too late. And thus the ancient patriarchs did practice, when the traveller and wayfaring men came by, they did not tarry till they came and asked relief and refreshment, but sat at the gates to watch for such, (*Judges 19. 20, 21*) and looked in the streets to find them, yea, set open their doors that they might freely and boldly enter in. And howsoever, some may think this too large a practice, since now the world is so full of people, yet I see not but the more people there is, the larger charity ought to be.

But be it so, as a man may neglect, in some sort the general world, yet those to whom he is bound, either in natural, civil, or religious bands, them he must seek how to do them good. A notable example you have in *David*, who, because there was twixt him and *Jonathan* a band and covenant, therefore he enquired, *Whether there was any left of the house of Saul, to whom he might shew mercy for Jonathan's sake*, 2 Sam. 9.1. So this people of *Corinth*, to whom *Paul* writeth, they were in a spiritual league and covenant in the *Gospel*, and so were a body. Now for one member in the body to seek himself, and neglect all others were, as if a man should clothe one arm or one leg of his body with gold and purple, and let all the rest of the members go naked. *1 Cor. 12. 27.*

Now brethren, I pray you, remember yourselves, and know, that you are not in a retired monastical course, but have given your names and promises one to another and covenanted here to cleave together in the service of God, and the King; What then must you do? May you live as retired hermits? and look after no body? Nay, you must seek still the wealth of one another; and enquire as *David*, how liveth such a man? How is he clad? How is he fed? He is my brother, my associate; we ventured our lives together here, and had a hard brunt of it and we are in league together. Is his labor harder than mine? surely I will ease him; hath he no bed to lie on? why, I have two, I'll lend him one; hath he no apparel? why, I have two suits, I'll give him one of them; eats he coarse fare, bread and water, and I have better, why, surely we will part stakes. He is as good a man as I, and we are bound each to other, so that his wants must be my wants, his sorrows my sorrows, his sickness my sickness, and his welfare my welfare, for I am as he is. And such a sweet sympathy were excellent, comfortable, yea, heavenly, and is the only maker and conserver of churches and commonwealths, and where this is wanting, ruin comes on quickly, as it did here in *Corinth*.

But besides these motives, there are other reasons to provoke us not only to do good one to another; but even to seek and search how to do it.

1. As first, to maintain modesty in all our associates, that of hungry wanters, they become not bold beggars and impudent cravers; for as one saith of women, that, when they have lost their shamefacedness, they have lost half their honesty, so may it be truly said of a man that when he hath lost his modesty, and puts on a begging face, he hath lost his majesty, and the image of that noble creature; and man should not beg and crave of man, but only of God. True it is, that as Christ was fain to crave water of the Samaritan woman, (*John 4. 5.*) so men are forced to ask sometimes rather than starve, but indeed in all societies it should be offered them. Men often complain of men's boldness in asking, but how cometh this to pass, but because the world have been so full of self-lovers as no man would offer their money, meat, garments, though they saw men hungry, harborless, poor, and naked in the streets; and what is it that makes men brazen-faced, bold, brutish, tumultuous, but because they are pinched with want, and see others of their companions (which it may be have less deserved) to live in prosperity and pleasure?

2. It wonderfully encourageth men in their duties, when they see the burthen equally borne; but when some withdraw themselves and retire to their own particular ease, pleasure, or profit; what heart can men have to go on in their business? when men are come together to lift some weighty piece of timber or vessel; if one stand still and do not lift, shall not the rest be weakened and disheartened? Will not a few idle drones spoil the whole stock of laborious bees: so one idle-belly, one murmurer, one complainer, one self-lover will weaken and dishearten a whole colony. Great matters have been brought to pass where men have cheerfully as with one heart, hand, and shoulder, gone about it, both in wars, buildings, and plantations, but where every man seeks himself, all cometh to nothing.

3. The present necessity requireth it, as it did in the days of the *Jews*, returning from captivity, and as it was here in *Corinth*. The country is yet raw, the land untilled, the cities not builded, the cattle not settled, we are compassed about with a helpless and idle people, the natives of the country, which cannot in any comely or comfortable manner help themselves, much less us. We also have been very chargeable to many of our loving friends, which helped us hither, and now again supplied us, so that before we think of gathering riches, we must even in conscience think of requiting their charge, love and labor, and cursed be that profit and gain which aimeth not at this. Besides, how many of our dear friends did here die at our first entrance, many of them no doubt for want of good lodging, shelter, and comfortable things, and many more may go after them quickly, if care be not taken. Is this then a time for men to begin to seek themselves? *Paul*

saith, that men in the last days shall be lovers of themselves, (*2 Tim. 3. 2.*) but it is here yet but the first days, and (as it were) the dawning of this new world, it is now therefore no time for men to look to get riches, brave clothes, dainty fare, but to look to present necessities; it is now no time to pamper the flesh, live at ease, snatch, catch, scrape, and pill, and hoard up, but rather to open the doors, the chests, and vessels, and say, brother, neighbor, friend, what want ye, any thing that I have? make bold with it, it is yours to command, to do you good, to comfort and cherish you, and glad I am that I have it for you.

4. And even the example of God himself, whom we should follow in all things within our power and capacity, may teach us this lesson, for (with reverence to his Majesty be it spoken) he might have kept all grace, goodness, and glory to himself, but he hath communicated it to us, even as far as we are capable of it in this life, and will communicate his glory in all fulness with his elect in that life to come; even so his son Jesus Christ left his glory eclipsed for a time, and abased himself to a poor and distressed life in this world, that he might, by it, bring us to happiness in the world to come. If God then have delighted in thus doing good and relieving frail and miserable man, so far inferior to himself, what delight ought man to have to relieve and comfort man, which is equal to himself?

5. Even as we deal with others, ourselves and others shall be dealt withal. Carest thou not how others fare, how they toil, are grieved, sick, pinched, cold, harborless, so as thou be in health, livest at ease, warm in thy nest, farest well? The days will come when thou shalt labor and none shall pity thee, be poor and none relieve thee, be sick, and lie and die and none visit thee, yea, and thy children shall lie and starve in the streets, and none shall relieve them, for *it is the merciful that shall obtain mercy*; Mat. 5. 7. and *the memory of the just shall be blessed* even in his seed; *Prov. 10.* and a merciful and loving man when he dies, though he leave his children small and desolate, yet every one is mercifully stirred up for the father's sake to shew compassion, but the unkindness, currishness, and self-love of a father, is through God's just judgment recompensed upon the children with neglect and cruelty.

6. Lastly, That we may draw to an end; A merciless man, and a man without natural affection or love, is reckoned among such as are given over of God to a reprobate mind, (*Rom. 1. 30.*) and (as it were) transformed into a beast-like humor; for, what is man if he be not sociable, kind, affable, free-hearted, liberal; he is a beast in the shape of a man; or rather an infernal spirit, walking amongst men, which makes the world a hell what in him lieth; for, it is even a hell to live where there are such men: such the Scriptures calleth *Nabals*, which signifieth *fools*, (*Psal. 14. 1.*) and decayed men, which have lost both the sap of grace and nature; and such merciless

men are called goats, and shall be set at Christ's left hand at the last day, (*Math. 25. 33.*) *Oh therefore seek the wealth one of another.*

Obj. But some will say, *It is true, and it were well if men would so do, but we see every man is so for himself, as that if I should not do so, I should do full ill, for if I have it not of my own, I may snap short sometimes, for I see no body showeth me any kindness, nor giveth me any thing; if I have gold or silver, that goeth for payment, and if I want it I may lie in the street, therefore I had best keep that I have, and not be so liberal as you would have me, except I saw others would be so towards me.*

Ans. This Objection seemeth but equal and reasonable, as did the Answer of *Nabal* to *David's* men, but it is most foolish and carnal, as his also was; for, if we should measure our courses by most men's practices, a man should never do any godly duty; for, do not the most, yea, almost all, go the broad way that leadeth to death and damnation, (*Luke. 13. 23, 24.*) Who then will follow a multitude? It is the word of God, and the examples of the best men that we must follow. And what if others will do nothing for thee, but are unkind and unmerciful to thee? Knowest thou not that they which will be the children of God must be kind to the unkind, loving to their enemies, and bless those that curse them? (*Mat. 5. 44, 47.*) If all men were kind to thee, it were but *publicans'* righteousness to be kind to them? If all men be evil, wilt thou be so too? When *David* cried out, *Help Lord, for not a godly man is left*, Psal. 12. 1. did he himself turn ungodly also? Nay, he was rather the more strict. So, if love and charity be departed out of this world, be thou one of them that shall first bring it in again.

And let this be the first rule, which I will with two others conclude for this time.

1. Never measure thy course by the most, but by the best, yea, and principally by God's word; Look not what others do to thee, but consider what thou art to do to them: seek to please God, not thyself. Did they in *Mat. 25. 44.* plead, that others did nothing for them? No such matter, no such plea will stand before God, his word is plain to the contrary, therefore, though all the world should neglect thee, disregard thee, and contemn thee, yet remember thou hast not to do with men, but with the highest God, and so thou must do thy duty to them notwithstanding.

2. And let there be no prodigal person to come forth and say, Give me the portion of lands and goods that appertaineth to me, and let me shift for myself; *Luke 15. 12.* It is yet too soon to put men to their shifts; *Israel* was seven years in *Canaan*, before the land was divided unto tribes, much longer before it was divided unto families; and why wouldst thou have thy particular portion, but because thou thinkest to live better than thy neighbor, and scornest to live so meanly as he? but who, I pray thee, brought this particularizing first into the world? Did not Satan, who was

not content to keep that equal state with his fellows, but would set his throne above the stars? Did not he also entice man to despise his general felicity and happiness, and go try particular knowledge of good and evil; and nothing in this world doth more resemble heavenly happiness, than for men to live as one, being of one heart, and one soul; neither any thing more resembles hellish horror, then for every man to shift for himself; for if it be a good mind and practise, thus to affect particulars, *mine* and *thine*, then it should be best also for God to provide one heaven for thee, and another for thy neighbor.

Object. But some will say, *If all men will do their endeavors as I do I could be content with this generality,—but many are idle and slothful, and eat up others' labors, and therefore it is best to part, and then every man may do his pleasure.*

First, this, indeed, is the common plea of such as will endure no inconveniences, and so for the hardness of men's hearts, God and man doth often give way to that which is not best, nor perpetual, but indeed if we take this course to change ordinances and practices because of inconveniences, we shall have every day new laws.

Secondly, if others be idle and thou diligent, thy fellowship, provocation, and example, may well help to cure that malady in them, being together, but being asunder, shall they not be more idle, and shall not gentry and beggary be quickly the glorious ensigns of your commonwealth?

Thirdly, construe things in the best part, be not too hasty to say, men are idle and slothful, all men have not strength, skill, faculty, spirit, and courage to work alike; it is thy glory and credit, that thou canst do so well, and his shame and reproach, that can do no better; and are not these sufficient rewards to you both.

Fourthly, if any be idle apparently, you have a law and governors to execute the same, and to follow that rule of the Apostle, to keep back their bread, and let them not eat, go not therefore whispering, to charge men with idleness; but go to the governor and prove them idle; and thou shall see them have their deserts. *Acts 19. 38. 2 Thes. 3. 10. Deut. 19. 15.*

And as you are a body together, so hang not together by skins and gymocks, but labor to be jointed together and knit by flesh and sinews; away with envy at the good of others, and rejoice in his good, and sorrow for his evil. Let his joy be thy joy, and his sorrow thy sorrow: Let his sickness be thy sickness: his hunger thy hunger: his poverty thy poverty; and if you profess friendship, be friends in adversity; for then a friend is known and tried, and not before.

3. Lay away all thought of former things and forget them, and think upon the things that are; look not gapingly one upon other, pleading your

goodness, your birth, your life you lived, your means you had and might have had; here you are by God's providence under difficulties; be thankful to God, it is no worse, and take it in good part that which is, and lift not up yourself because of former privileges; when *Job* was brought to the dung-hill, he sat down upon it, *Job 2. 8.* and when the Almighty had been bitter to *Naomi*, she would be called *Marah*; consider therefore what you are now, and whose you are; say not I could have lived thus, and thus; but say thus and thus I must live: for God and natural necessity requireth, if your difficulties be great, you had need to cleave the faster together, and comfort and cheer up one another, laboring to make each other's burden lighter; there is no grief so tedious as a churlish companion and nothing makes sorrows easy more than cheerful associates: bear ye therefore one another's burthen, and be not a burthen one to another; avoid all factions, frowardness, singularity and withdrawings, and cleave fast to the Lord, and one to another continually; so shall you be a notable precedent to these poor heathens, whose eyes are upon you, and who very brutishly and cruelly do daily eat and consume one another, through their emulations, ways and contentions; be you therefore ashamed of it, and win them to peace both with yourselves, and one another, by your peaceable examples, which will preach louder to them, than if you could cry in their barbarous language; so also shall you be an encouragement to many of your christian friends in your native country, to come to you, when they hear of your peace, love and kindness that is amongst you: but above all, it shall go well with your souls, when that God of peace and unity shall come to visit you with death as he hath done many of your associates, you being found of him, not in murmurings, discontent and jars, but in brotherly love, and peace, may be translated from this wandering wilderness unto that joyful and heavenly Canaan.

AMEN.